How to use this book

Follow the advice, in italics, given for you on each page.
Support the children as they read the text that is shaded in cream.
Praise *the children at every step!*

Detailed guidance is provided in the Read Write Inc. Phonics Handbook

8 reading activities

Children:
- *Practise reading the speed sounds.*
- *Read the green and red words for the story.*
- *Listen as you read the introduction.*
- *Discuss the vocabulary check with you.*
- *Read the story.*
- *Re-read the story and discuss the 'questions to talk about'.*
- *Re-read the story with fluency and expression.*
- *Practise reading the speed words.*

Speed sounds

Consonants *Say the pure sounds (do not add 'uh').*

f (ff)	l ll	m mm	n nn kn	r rr	s ss	v ve	z zz s	sh	th	ng nk

b bb	c k ck	d dd	g gg	h	j	p pp	qu	t tt	w wh	x	y	ch tch

Vowels *Say the sounds in and out of order.*

at	hen head	in	on	up	day	see happy	high	blow

zoo	look	car	for	fair	whirl	shout	boy

*Each box contains one sound but sometimes more than one grapheme. Focus graphemes are **circled**.*

4

Green words

milk   fi**sh**   sni**ff**   **qu**i**ck**   nap   stre**tch**   box

ki**tt**`en → ki**tt**en     a`lo**ng** → alo**ng**

trot   →   trots   run   →   runs   stand   →   stands

dri**nk**   →   dri**nk**s

Red words

he   **sh**e   to   No   ca**ll**   h**er**   **th**e   I'**ve**

Vocabulary check

Discuss the meaning (as used in the story) after the children have read each word.

definition:

nap   *a short sleep*

trot   *walk quickly*

Finn   *Meg's fluffy case for pyjamas in the shape of a cat*

Punctuation to note in this story:

Meg Finn Tab	*Capital letters for names*
Yes Is The	*Capital letters that start sentences*
.	*Full stop at the end of each sentence*
!	*Exclamation mark used to show excitement*
...	*Wait and see*

Tab's kitten

Introduction

Do you love fluffy kittens?
Tab the cat has just had a kitten. She is very protective of
her kitten and keeps an eye on him all the time. However,
one day she falls asleep and the kitten disappears.

Story written by Gill Munton
Illustrated by Tim Archbold

Tab the cat has had a kitten.

"Tab! Tab!

I've got fish and milk!"

calls Meg.

Tab trots to Meg.

The kitten trots along as well.

sniff
sniff

Tab has the fish.

The kitten drinks the milk.

Tab's tum is full.

She has a quick nap.

The kitten runs off.

Tab stands up to stretch her long legs.

No kitten!

Is he in the box?

No!

Is he in the bath?

No!

Is he on Meg's bed?

No ...

Yes, he is!

He is with Finn!

Questions to talk about

Re-read the page. Read the question to the children. Tell them whether it is a **FIND IT** question or **PROVE IT** question.

FIND IT

✓ Turn to the page

✓ Read the question

✓ Find the answer

PROVE IT

✓ Turn to the page

✓ Read the question

✓ Find your evidence

✓ Explain why

Page 8:	FIND IT	What does Meg call out to Tab?
Page 10:	FIND IT	What noise does the kitten make as he drinks his milk?
Page 11:	FIND IT	What does the kitten do while Tab has a sleep?
Page 12:	FIND IT	Tab is shocked when she wakes up. No kitten. Where does she look?
Page 13:	FIND IT	Where does Tab find her kitten?
Page 13:	PROVE IT	Why do you think he curls up with Finn?